Kipper wanted a magic adventure but
the magic key would not glow. It had not
glowed for a long time.

"Maybe it will glow if I keep it with me,"
he thought, so he put it in his pocket.

Mum had to go shopping. She wanted
Kipper to go with her.

"I want to get you some new trainers,"
she said, "so come on."

Kipper forgot he had the key in his pocket.

OXFORD
UNIVERSITY PRESS

On the way to the shops, Mum let
Kipper stop and play. He ran to the rocket
and the key fell out of his pocket and on to
the grass.

"Look at me, Mum!" he called.

Kipper looked in his pockets but the key was not there.

"Oh no!" said Kipper. "Where is the key? I can't have lost it, can I?"
But he had lost the key.

OXFORD
UNIVERSITY PRESS

Kipper wanted to go and look for the key, but Mum would not let him. It had started to rain and Mum wanted to get home.

"Ask Biff and Chip to look for it," she said.

A man came to cut the grass. He cut it with a mower. The mower ran over the magic key with a clang.

"What was that?" said the man.

OXFORD
UNIVERSITY PRESS

The key had broken the mower.

"Grrrrr!" the man said, crossly. "Now I shall have to mend the mower."
He was so cross that he threw the magic key in a bin.

Two boys came to play on the swings.
One of the boys looked in the bin and
found the key.

"Look at this old, bent key," he said.
"What shall we do with it?"

OXFORD
UNIVERSITY PRESS

The boys took the key with them. One of them had some string. He tied the key to the string and spun it round and round.

Suddenly the string broke and the key
flew through the air. It hit a greenhouse
with a crash and broke the glass.

"Oh no!" said the boys.

OXFORD
UNIVERSITY PRESS

"Look at my greenhouse!" yelled the
man. "The glass is broken."
The boys ran away as fast as they could.
　"Just you come back here," called the
man.

Kipper had to tell Biff and Chip that he
had lost the magic key.

"I think I lost it by the rocket," he said,
"but Mum wouldn't let me look for it."

"Come on," said Chip. "We must find
it."

OXFORD
UNIVERSITY PRESS

Wilf and Wilma helped them look for the lost key. Biff asked the man if he had seen it.

"Yes," said the man. "I threw it in that bin, but two boys took it out."

The children saw the two boys. They asked them if they had found the key.

"Yes," said the boys, "but we lost it again. We broke a man's greenhouse with it."

OXFORD
UNIVERSITY PRESS

They saw the man with the greenhouse.
"We are sorry about the broken glass,"
said Chip, "but could we have the key?"

"Sorry," said the man. "I sold the key to
the junk shop to help pay for the glass."

The children went to the junk shop. They told the lady about the key and asked her if she had it.

"Sorry," said the lady. "I have just sold it."

OXFORD
UNIVERSITY PRESS

The lady told them who had it.

"A man came in," she said. "He wanted some old keys."

She told them that the man had a shop down the street.

The children went to the man's shop. In the window there were pictures and paintings.

"Why do you think the man wants old keys?" asked Wilf.

OXFORD
UNIVERSITY PRESS

Wilma looked inside the shop. It was closed and she couldn't see the man.

"We must get our pocket money," said Biff. "We may have to buy the key back."

"Let's go home, then," said Chip.

Mum went to the shop with the children. She told the man about the key and how Kipper had lost it. She asked if they could have the key back.

"Yes," said the man. "If you can find it."

OXFORD
UNIVERSITY PRESS

The man had painted some pictures and had put lots of keys in them. All the keys had been painted. The children looked at the pictures but they couldn't see the magic key.

They looked at all the pictures.

"All the keys look the same," said Biff.
Suddenly Kipper saw a little picture. It had
one key in it.

"Here it is," he said. "This is our key."

OXFORD
UNIVERSITY PRESS

The man told them that they would
have to buy the picture. Biff and Chip gave
Mum their pocket money, and Mum paid
the man.

"It's a lot to pay for an old key," she
said.

The children pulled the key from the picture and rubbed off the paint. Then they looked at it.

"The key has not glowed for a long time," said Biff. "Perhaps it has lost its magic."

OXFORD
UNIVERSITY PRESS

"It's been out in the rain," said Wilf,
"and it's been bent by a mower."

"It's been through a window," said Chip,
"and it's been stuck on a painting."

"It's had a bad time," said Wilma.

The children wanted the key to glow.
Wilma picked it up.

"Do you think it will ever glow again?"
she said. "Do you think the magic will still
work?"

"I don't know," said Biff. "I hope so."

OXFORD
UNIVERSITY PRESS

But the key didn't glow and the magic wouldn't work. Kipper told the key about the adventures he would like to have. But still the magic wouldn't work.

The next day, Wilf and Wilma came to the house with Nadim and Anneena. The children were sorry about the key. It still wouldn't glow and they were all very sad.

"How can we make the magic work
again?" asked Wilma.

Anneena thought of a good idea.

"Let's remind it of the magic
adventures," she said. "Maybe that will
make it work."

But the key still didn't glow. At last the children gave up. Mum told Biff and Chip it was time for their friends to go home. "Cheer up," said Mum.

Kipper was sorry about the key.

"It's all my fault," he said and he began
to cry.

"Don't cry, Kipper," said Chip. "Maybe
the magic has just run out."

Biff and Chip let Kipper take the key to bed. Kipper looked at it for a long time. At last he fell asleep. Suddenly, the magic key began to glow.

OXFORD
UNIVERSITY PRESS